...ars old.

My birthday is
_____

This fantastic
Brownie Annual 2002
belongs to

_____

Turn the page for masses more fun.

Safety first!

You should be able to have a go at everything in your great annual, but sometimes it's wise to ask an adult you know for help. You can still do it by yourself, just make sure the adult says it's okay and is watching what you do. There is a note on some pages reminding you when you are likely to need help. If there isn't a symbol but you still aren't sure, ask for help anyway.

Brownie fun

Brownies have an amazing time doing masses of exciting activities. There are lots of great reasons to be a Brownie!

Badge work

On most of the pages of your fabulous *Brownie Annual 2002* there is a badge work box. The badges show where activities and ideas fit into the Brownie programme. If you want to find out what you need to do to get an interest badge, look it up in your *Brownie Guide Badge Book*. For most badges there are quite a few things you have to do, but the most important thing is to always do your best.

Go! is a great part of the Brownie programme. You need to be nine years old to start it, but don't let this stop you having a go at pages with this badge!

These badges show the parts of the Brownie Guide programme that are covered on the page.

Brownies are friendly

Brownies have fun out-of-doors

Brownies keep healthy

Brownies make things

Brownies are wide awake

Brownies help at home

Brownies lend a hand

Brownies do their best

Photographs by Kelvin Rogers

Brownie
Annual 2002

Brownie Guide Promise
I promise that I will do my best:
To love my God,
To serve the Queen and my country,
To help other people
and
To keep the Brownie Guide Law.

Brownie Guide Motto
Lend A Hand.

Brownie Guide Law
A Brownie Guide thinks of others before herself and does a Good Turn every day.

THE GUIDE ASSOCIATION
A registered charity

www.guides.org.uk

Web safe
My Brownie code for safety on the World Wide Web. I promise that:

⚜ I will agree with my parents'/guardians' rules for me using a computer, and the World Wide Web.

⚜ I will not give my address or my telephone number without permission.

⚜ I will not give my school's name and address without permission.

⚜ I will say 'No' if anyone who I've met on the World Wide Web wants to meet me, unless my parent(s)/guardian(s) have agreed and will go with me.

⚜ I won't put my photograph on a web site.

⚜ I will tell my parent(s)/guardian(s) or teacher if I discover something on the World Wide Web which worries or upsets me.

With thanks to the Girl Scouts of the USA for the initial ideas contained within this warning for children.

Contents

The Brownie Guides who appear in this Annual are from 1st Pilgrim's Hatch Brownie Pack and 1st Hackney Brownie Pack.

Clothes Brownies' own or from The Guide Association Trading Service (for details call 0800 838227 or visit www.guidingessentials.org.uk) or New Look (for stockists call 0500 454094).

 THE GUIDE ASSOCIATION TRADING SERVICE NEW LOOK

Super Brownie's new friend written by Marion Thompson; A special Brownie compiled by Wendy Watts; A helping hand written by Jenny Wackett.

Cover photograph by Kelvin Rogers; Brownie photographs by Diana Aynaci, Moose Azim and Kelvin Rogers; Guide photographs by Moose Azim and Kelvin Rogers.

Brownie Annual 2002

© The Guide Association 2001

All Brownie and Guide photographs © The Guide Association; all other photographs © as acknowledged on appropriate pages. 'S-T-R-E-T-C-H--I-N-G' © Sharon Cheeks appears in CADBURY'S SECOND SELECTION OF CHILDREN'S POETRY, reproduced by

permission of Cadbury Ltd. 'Snowy' © 1998 John Nevinson appears in STORY OF THE YEAR 6 published by Scholastic Ltd, reproduced by permission of the publisher.

Published by The Guide Association (a registered charity), 17–19 Buckingham Palace Road, London SW1W 0PT E-mail chq@guides.org.uk Website www.guides.org.uk ISBN 0 85260 170 0 The Guide Association Trading Service ordering code 6005

 **THE GUIDE ASSOCIATION** *A registered charity*

An official publication of The Guide Association (incorporated by Royal Charter, registered charity number 306016).

Readers are reminded that during the life span of this publication there may be changes to The Guide Association's policy, or legal requirements, that will affect the accuracy of the information contained within these pages.

Patrons HM The Queen, HM Queen Elizabeth, The Queen Mother President HRH The Princess Margaret, Countess of Snowdon World Chief

Guide (1930–1977) Olave, Lady Baden-Powell, GBE Chief Guide Jenny Leach Brownie Guide Adviser Sandra Moffitt Publications Manager Anne Moffat Project Editor Alice Forbes Design Team Manager Gillian Webb Special Project Designer David Jones Designers Tracey Goutis, Cathy Summers Production Stuart Poole Colour repro Magnet Harlequin Printed and bound DeAgostini

All illustrations and photographs as acknowledged on appropriate pages.

7

Get your

Be safe
Wear safety clothing like elbow and knee pads, wrist guards and a helmet that fits. ❋ Good safety clothing is not just about padding but should help you slide safely without grazing yourself. ❋ Be seen. Wear light, bright clothing. ❋ Don't skate after dark. ❋ Be alert to what other people are doing around you. Don't carry anything but yourself on your skates! ❋ Get an adult to check that you are safe before setting off.

In-line skating, or rollerblading, is one of the fastest growing sports today. It's easy and it's fun. Give it a go.

Where to go
Do not skate on pavements or the road. Stick to skating areas in parks or recreation areas. Pick a nice smooth level surface. Avoid wet surfaces. Watch out for pebbles, twigs, oily patches and other hazards. Only skate indoors at a proper rollerblading centre.

What to wear
In-line skates should have proper ankle support. Make sure they are a snug fit, but not tight. They shouldn't be loose round the heel. Check buckles, straps and laces are in good condition. Elbow and knee pads, and wrist guards should be the right size and give good side protection. Make sure all the straps are in good condition. It is all right to wear a cycling helmet as a safety helmet provided it fits. Make sure your other clothes aren't too baggy or get in the way of the skates. It's best to make sure your skin is covered in case you fall over.

Getting going
Anyone can have fun rollerblading, but check with an adult first if you have back problems or find balancing hard. It is a great way to get fit and can be hard work, so you should make sure you don't have any injuries before you start.

Making a stand
Stand up slowly, moving on to your knees. Rest your hands on your knees keeping your knees slightly bent. Put your weight on the balls of your feet. Keep your head up and look in the direction you want to go. If you look at the ground, that's where you'll end up! Stay relaxed. Try a couple of easy knee bends.

Stop the wobble
At any point if you feel wobbly try to bend your knees slightly and put your hands on them. This should stop you falling backwards and give you a moment to get wobble-free again.

skates on!

Practise tips

Try some of the moves without your skates on if you want. Get a feel for what your doing on a level surface that you won't roll away on, like grass.

First steps

Try to keep your feet about shoulder-width apart. Take a very small step keeping your knees bent. Then step back to where you were. Now try it with your other foot. Use your arms for balance.

Walking

Turn your toes out so your feet make a V shape. Keep your weight more on the inside of your skates. Start to 'walk' by sliding your feet in small steps. Remember to keep your knees bent. Look where you are going and use your arms to balance. Think about keeping your weight forward. Try using your thigh muscles to 'walk'.

Gliding

Take two or three steps with your toes out. On the final steps end up with your feet straight. Keep your knees bent with your hands on them. Look forward and glide. When you slow down take a few more steps with your toes out, then get into the gliding position again.

Easy fall

You may fall over quite a bit to start with so it's a good idea to know how to fall properly. Keep your elbows and knees bent. Your knee pads and wrist guards should slide well on the surface. Keep your hands open so your palms slide along. Try to stay floppy and relaxed.

Stopping

To stop without using the brake on your skates, turn your toes to make a backward V shape. You may need to try to get your feet further apart. Keep your knees bent and your weight on the inside of your skates. You will grind to a halt.

Whale of a time

Whales are massive animals. Some of them are the largest creatures that have ever lived. Find out about their underwater life.

Mammals not fish

Unlike fish, whales do not breathe through gills. They have got to come to the surface of the water to breathe air. Like mammals, they do not lay eggs but give birth to live young and the mother feeds them on her milk.

ALL shapes and sizes

Whales are found all over the world and there are almost 80 species. At over 30 metres long, the blue whale is even larger than the biggest dinosaurs that ever lived. The smallest members of the whale family are dolphins which are about two metres long.

Eating

There are two main ways whales eat. Some, like dolphins and sperm whales, have teeth and they feed on fish and squid. Others filter mouthfuls of water through sieve-like 'baleen' in their mouths to get tiny fish and shrimps.

All photographs supplied by Oxford Scientific Films: background whale Daniel J Cox; bottlenose dolphin Chris McLaughlin; whale surfacing to blow Ben Osborne; whale tail Michele Hall; mother and calf David B Fleetham; breaching whale James Watt.

Blow holes

A whale's blow hole lets it breathe through the top of its head. When it comes to the surface, the whale breathes out very quickly. This looks like a jet of water, but it's stale air with a fine misty spray that can reach four metres high. The whale breathes in again and the blow hole shuts before the whale submerges.

Tail powered

Whales are very strong swimmers and can travel thousands of kilometres between feeding areas and where they breed. It is mainly the muscles in the last third of a whale's body that power the enormous tail. The tail pushes the whale through the water, like a swimmer's feet. The two halves of the tail are called flukes. Some whales have unique markings on them like fingerprints.

Biggest whale

The blue whale does not hunt for its food. It has baleen, so as it swims it simply gulps huge amounts of water that it filters for shrimps. Blue whales give birth to a baby about the size of an elephant. The baby whale drinks about 100 litres of milk a day. By the time it is six months old it is 16 metres long.

Whale sounds

Scientists are only just beginning to understand the sounds that whales make. Male humpback whales can 'sing' for hours to try to find a female mate. Some whales also breach, or leap out of the water then splash down on the surface. When they do this, or slap their tails on the water's surface, they may be trying to communicate with other whales. Other whales, such as dolphins, 'talk' using a clicking sound.

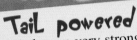

Families

Most whales live together in large family groups. Often the females will share looking after the young. The group often work together to round up fish or look out for dangers. These groups are usually called pods.

Food for sport

Eating the right food is important to make sure you stay healthy and to give you energy. So take a look at these yummy ideas.

Top tips

Ask an adult to help you in the kitchen. ✿ Always wash your hands before cooking. ✿ Tie back long hair.

Fruit faces

Ingredients
230g strawberries ✳ 250ml yoghurt ✳ 25g sugar ✳ satsuma or clementine ✳ 2 glacé cherries ✳ 4 grapes

You need
chopping board ✳ knife ✳ mixing bowl ✳ potato masher ✳ spoon ✳ 2 dishes

1 Wash the strawberries. Cut each one in half. Remove the stalk and core.

2 Mash the strawberries until they are smooth.

3 Add the yoghurt and the sugar. Stir well. Pour into two dishes, then leave in the fridge for ten minutes.

4 Peel the satsuma. Remove as much pith as possible from two segments. Wash the grapes.

5 Place the cherries, satsuma segments and grapes on each yoghurt mix to make a face.

Cook's know-how
Try using a foodmixer to make the yoghurt mixture.

Baked energy

Ingredients
1 baked potato ✱ butter
✱ 60g grated cheese ✱ tomato

You need
baking tray ✱ knife ✱ spoon
✱ bowl ✱ fork or masher ✱
chopping board ✱ oven gloves

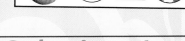
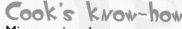
1 Pre-heat the oven to 200°C/gas mark 6. Lightly grease a baking tray.

Cook's know-how
Microwaving the potatoes makes this quicker.

2 Let the potato cool then cut it in half. Scoop out the middle into the bowl.

3 Add two dabs of butter then mash. Fill the potato skins with the mixture.

4 Top with grated cheese. Slice the tomato and put three slices on top of each potato.

5 Place on the baking tray then pop in the oven for 15–20 minutes.

Funny faces
Use raspberries, blackcurrants or two small bananas instead of strawberries. ✱ Experiment with different fruit to make the faces. Take a look at the ideas below.

Great toppings!
Tuna mixed with sweetcorn and a little mayonnaise. ✱ Baked beans. ✱ Coleslaw. ✱ Just with a blob of butter. ✱ Spaghetti hoops. ✱ Chopped ham and cheese.

Blackberry yoghurt mixture with raspberry eyes, a choccy nose and a banana for the mouth.

Banana yoghurt mixture with kiwi fruit eyes, strawberry nose and chocolate drop mouth.

13

S-t-r-e-t

Waking up
in the morning
is lovely.
Especially when you s-t-r-e-t-c-h.
You open up
your legs and arms
and stretch.
It's just lovely.
The feeling just makes
you want to do it
over and over again.
But after a while
your stretch
runs out
and it's over.

Sharon Cheeks

Illustrated by Stuart Lynch

-c-h-i-n-g

Fever pitch

Start having some footie fun right now with these great puzzles.

Spot the ball
How many footballs can you spot?

Odd ball
Which ball is the odd one out?

Illustrated by Phil Dobson

16

Find it out

Find these top football words in the square on the right.

Team
Match
Score

Dribble
Kick-off
Off-side
Penalty
Red card
Referee
Striker

Defender
Division
Football
Linesman
World Cup

Centre half
Goalkeeper
Yellow card

T	E	A	M	P	E	N	A	L	T	Y	V
M	O	L	C	D	E	F	E	N	D	E	R
K	S	N	E	O	D	R	I	B	B	L	E
I	L	I	N	E	S	M	A	N	F	L	M
C	Q	P	T	D	I	V	I	S	I	O	N
K	S	T	R	I	K	E	R	J	H	W	O
O	F	R	E	D	C	A	R	D	T	C	F
F	W	V	H	S	C	O	R	E	K	A	F
F	G	O	A	L	K	E	E	P	E	R	S
W	O	R	L	D	C	U	P	B	B	D	I
C	S	F	F	O	O	T	B	A	L	L	D
M	A	T	C	H	R	E	F	E	R	E	E

Get the goal

Find the right path the player must take to score a goal.

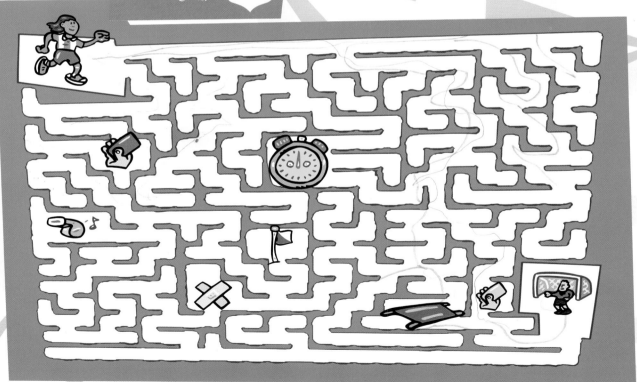

How did you score?
Find out on page 76.

17

Staple food

Rice is eaten in Japan and South Korea, as well as being really popular all over the world. Find out more about how it is cooked and is grown.

Rice dishes

Rice doesn't taste of much by itself, but can be used in lots of ways. How about puffed rice for breakfast? Or rice pudding? Boiled with spices, like pilau rice from India? It can make a tasty Italian risotto, or be cooked with fish and vegetables for a Japanese sushi. It is used in Caribbean jambalya and Spanish paella. Have you ever eaten rice paper, or rice noodles?

Different types

There are different types of rice, each one good for these different types of cooking. Take a look in your supermarket. You'll see there is long grain and short grain, as well as brown and white. Some have other names, like wild rice or aborio.

Cooking

All rice needs to be properly rinsed before it is cooked. Then it has to be boiled so the hard dry grains can be eaten. Sometimes rice is then fried, such as egg-fried rice. After boiling, long-grain rice tends to get fluffy, while short-grain rice gets sticky.

What is rice?

Rice is a cereal, like wheat, corn or barley. The grains are the seeds of the rice plant. When it grows, the grain is protected by a husk. The rice you buy has been milled to remove the husks.

Planting rice

Rice grains are first planted in normal soil. When they have grown about 20 centimetres tall, they are planted in special fields called paddy fields. There is plenty of space between each plant so it has room to grow and it is easier to weed the fields. In some parts of the world, rice planting is done by hand. It is very hard work.

Paddy fields

The paddy fields have been ploughed before the rice is planted. Although they may look like lakes, the fields are specially flooded to a certain level. The water usually comes from a stream. Special walls and ditches mean that fresh water is flowing into the fields all the time.

Harvesting

The rice plants grow quite tall and turn golden brown. They are then ready to harvest. The paddy field is drained and the ground allowed to harden. The crop is cut, then the grains are separated from the stalks. This is called threshing. Farmers without harvesting or threshing machines do all this by hand.

Rice facts

Over half the people in the world rely on the rice every day as part of their staple diet. ★ Rice is grown all over the world, including many Asian countries, North and South America, Europe and Africa. ★ Rice belongs to the food group called carbohydrates, like potatoes, pasta and bread. ★ Each grain of rice is a seed, and can be grown into a rice plant. ★ At weddings, rice is sometimes thrown over the bride for luck.

Milling

After the final bits of dirt and stalk are removed, the grains are dried so they won't rot. Before the grain is sold as food, it must be milled to remove the outer husk. Sometimes rice is further ground to make a flour.

Woven friendship

Have a go at this great jewellery idea.
These bracelets are fun to make and you
can choose your own colours.

You need
4 pieces thin wool or
embroidery thread, each
1.5m long ❖ safety pin

This bracelet uses red, white, purple
and green thread, but you can swap
these for your favourite colours.

1 Fold the threads in half.
Tie a knot about 1cm from
the end.

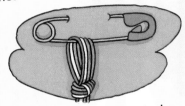

2 Thread the pin through the
loop. Carefully attach it to the
knee of your trousers.

3 Sort out any tangles and
arrange the threads as shown.

4 Loop the left red twice round
the white. Push the loops firmly
and gently make a little knot.

5 Now loop the red
twice round the purple.
Make sure the knot is
tight against the first one.

6 Loop the red round the green.
Make the knot tight against the
one before. Sort out any tangles
in the threads.

7 Loop the right red twice
round the white. Notice the
knot is the other way round
to before.

8 Now loop it round the purple and knot it firmly.

9 Finally loop it round the green to make the third knot on the right.

12 Loop the white round the green. Knot it closely to the one above and the one before.

10 Take the left red and loop it twice round the other red. Pull it firmly into a knot. Sort out any tangles.

11 Start again on the left. Loop the white round the purple. Make a firm knot as close to the one above as you can.

13 Finally knot the white round the red, before sorting out any tangles.

14 Go to the right and knot the white round the purple, then the green and finally the red. Each time make sure the knot is snug to the one above and the one before.

15 Take the left white. Knot it round the right white. Pull it firmly into position.

16 Sort out any tangles and gently push the two rows of knots flat.

Keep working the strands from the outside left to the middle. Then from the outside right to the middle. Finally do the centre knot. Gently press it flat from time to time and keep untangling the threads as you need to.

When it is long enough to go round your wrist, knot the two strands. Then plait them for about 4cm. Tie a knot at the end of each one.

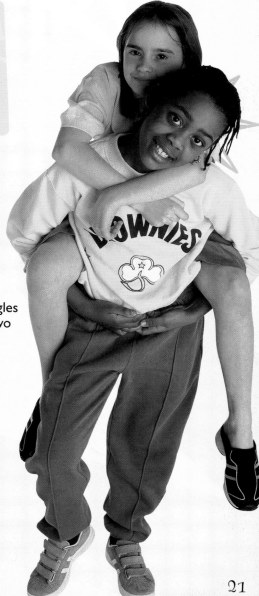

21

Snowy

I'm always scared. Scared of everything. My big brother Phil says I'm frightened of my own shadow.

Scared of everything, big and small. I go the long way to school so I don't have to pass that big dog at number 27 or the crazy old lady with the cats at number 39 who plays her piano all night. But if I go the short way to school I still have to pass the Armstrong twins' house, and they sat me in the road once and pushed snow down my ears. The Farrell kids saw them and they've called me Snowy ever since.

And even when I get to school, I get scared. I stay away from the Armstrong twins in the playground, as well as the kids in the different gangs. I hide from a parent called Mrs Harrison because she says I deliberately took her Martin's lunch-box, but it was the same colour as mine and didn't have a name on, so it was a mistake.

Then when the teacher comes out for us to line up an nine o'clock, I don't want to be chosen to walk down the corridor to ring the In-Time bell for her, just in case I do it wrong, so I don't catch her eye by staring at the map of Britain painted on the ground.

All those dots on the map. G for Glasgow, N for Newcastle, L for Liverpool... Are there as many scared people living in each of those little dots? Are there lots of children just like me, all over Britain?

Then I get into school. I like so much of it but I can't enjoy it because I'm scared about things coming along that I don't like. I mean, we don't have swimming till Thursday but I worry about it even on Monday, and by Wednesday my stomach feels like a big achy hole. I'm not just scared of the water and the loud instructor with a face the colour of ham, but I worry if I'll be the last ready to get on the coach for school, so I struggle to get my socks on to wet feet, and they stick, and I panic, and people shout, "There's just one person still changing," to the teacher, and that's me, and I panic more... It's really horrible.

And it's not just swimming. Friday morning is spelling test and tables test. I usually get full marks but I'm always worried that I might not manage it. And I'm scared of looking after the class goldfish in case I have to clean the tank and might need to hold the slippery, delicate thing. And once I misread the thermometer and spoiled the whole class's weather records on temperatures.

My mum says, "Stop worrying." My dad just sighs. My brother Phil is a teenager so naturally says kind things like, "Don't be so wet, you wally!"

So I woke up yesterday and immediately thought of all the scary things which would probably happen today, Tuesday. No baths, no spellings. But we were having a visitor in to talk to us about animals, and my teacher said he'll have some in boxes or cages, and already I'm dreading that the visitor will say, "Hold this giant Indian spider," or let a hawk fly round the room, and it'll settle on my shoulder, and... and...

Dad's car is away down the road as I get up. Phil is in the bathroom sploshing and gurgling before his usual mad dash to the school bus. Mum helps at the old folks' home, and leaves just after me, but she smiles as I check everything five times – packed lunch-box, hankie, reading book...

I get a peck on the cheek from her. A peck on the cheek reminds me of the animal visitor. Will the eagle or the vulture give me a real peck on the cheek?

I start to go the long way round, to avoid the dog at 27 and the crazy piano lady at 39, but then I see a large woman marching along a child with a green lunch-box, and it's Mrs Harrison who says I stole it, and I don't want to meet her, so my stomach does a big jump as I turn to go the other way to school.

I pass number 27, and there's no sign of that dog. I'm in luck, I think. It must be because it's the seventh day of the month, and seven is a lucky number. I reach the next danger spot, number 39.

This is where old Mrs Stewart lives. Her front garden is like a jungle of matted brown grass, and her straggly privet is too high for even my dad to see over. Late at night, she plays the piano loudly, no tune, just a thundering rumble. Her lights are on, the curtains open, but nobody can see her through the forest of hedge. Sometimes, Mrs Stewart just leans on her brush, looking up the road. Our Phil says her husband was killed in Hitler's war and never came home, but she looks up the road waiting for him to appear. It's sad, I should feel sorry for her, but I'm too scared of her to feel sad.

I've never heard a barking like it. I'm right outside number 39 and the dog from number 27 is suddenly there in front of me. It's a big brown Alsatiany-wolfy thing with huge yellow teeth and a slobbering pink tongue. He hates me. I think he knows that I was glad when he was knocked down by the ice-cream van last summer. I can still see the damaged fur on his back where he was cut. Roscoe, he's called, but I don't know why.

Roscoe snarls and moves towards me. I feel like my feet are glued to the pavement. My brain wants my body to move somewhere safe. Suddenly, I

shoot into a dark patch of shady grass behind a high hedge. Safe. Even Roscoe won't come after me here. He slopes off, looking back and barking in disappointment.

I'm safe. Then I realise where I am. I'm standing in crazy Mrs Stewart's jungle. And I can hear a voice calling Snowy. That's the horrible name that the Farrells call me. But they're at school by now, so who can it be? Suddenly, out of the front door comes the mad old lady calling Snowy.

At first, I'm scared, as usual. Then I'm really scared. Have the horrible Farrells told Mrs Stewart my nickname is Snowy? Is everyone in this street against me?

Then I realise that the old lady is crying when she says Snowy. Big tears are rolling down her pink cheeks, and she pushes back her snow-white hair with an old veined hand. "Snowy, oh Snowy," she sobs.

Turn the page to find out how the story ends.

Now, all at once, I feel so sorry for the old lady that I forget all the stories about her which Phil told to scare me. I go up to her, and say stupidly, "Snowy?" She turns her sad old blue eyes to me, and looks so confused and lost that I just find myself taking her old hand, and hear myself saying, "What's wrong?"

"Snowy," she says. How does she know that people laughingly call me that?

"Snowy," I say to her, because I can't think what else to say.

"Snowy?" she says again. Anyone listening to this strange conversation on the other side of the hedge would think we were crazy, Mrs Stewart and me.

But when she says Snowy again, I realize that she's not really looking at me, but sort of through me, like I was invisible. I find myself turning, and see, perched on the top of a rickety wooden shed roof, a dirty white ball of straggly fur.

"Snowy," she murmurs, and I say Snowy again because now I realize what the old lady is upset about. Her old cat Snowy is stuck on the rotten roof of the shed with his paw caught in a hole, and it's yowling away making noises like, "Maaaaa-am."

I find myself walking over to the metal dustbin, and hoisting myself on to it. (Me, who won't go on the climbing frame at school!) I can't reach the unhappy fur bundle, so I scramble back down, look through the dirty brown windows of the shed, and see a ladder in the gloom. I walk in. Mrs Stewart just watches me, still saying Snowy.

I drag out the ladder and prop it against the wall. The shed creaks as my weight comes against it, and the ladder complains, too. I get to the top of the steps and reach across the roof. Snowy spits and bats his open claws at me, and I notice a look of hate in his sharp green eyes. I also notice blood on his leg, caught in the hole in the roof, and see that each time he scrabbles to get free, he jams it further into the splintered space.

Now I'm on the roof and my feet have left the ladder which sways and falls with a crash into a bank of green nettles. The roof isn't nice and firm like a pavement, it sort of dinges in like the mattress on my bed. I feel quite sick. But with excitement. I'm amazed. I'm not scared at all. Everything is so unreal and like a dream. Me, up a ladder on the crazy lady's shed roof, rescuing her vicious cat, and I don't feel scared at all!

As I hear my voice say firmly, "Snowy!" I reach out and the terrified creature leaves a pattern of red scratches across my hand which start to ooze blood. But I'm determined to grab Snowy before he slides through the hole in the roof, which is

Illustrated by Jan Fearnley

24

getting larger. I know if it falls though, the cat will be hurt, and perhaps break bones. I don't seem to have time to think about any bones which I might break.

All this time, Mrs Stewart has been moaning "Snowy". Now I suddenly hear a man's voice, sharp and Scottish, saying, "Stay still, don't move!" Before I can turn my head, I hear a swish of nettles as the ladder is pulled out of them, and a bang as it's pushed against the shed. A strong hand touches my foot, and the voice says, "You're okay. I'll see to this cat. Well done. It was a brave try."

In the next whirling seconds, the man has the cat, which seems too surprised to scratch him, and he puts it on the path. It scampers past Mrs Stewart, who follows it into the dark hallway of the house. The man helps me down the ladder. I don't know what to say to him. Perhaps I'm in trouble for climbing on the roof and damaging it, so I run past the white van which he must have parked outside number 39, and dash off to school. I mustn't be late, oh no, I mustn't be late. I'm always scared of being late.

I'm there just in time, but I'm so flustered and hot that the teacher on duty sees my scratched hand and gets the Welfare Lady to clean it. She wants to know what happened but I can't explain. I want to be in my classroom before the door closes, so I won't have to walk into the room in front of them all, and perhaps be late for the register.

I'm just in time. It's a rushed register because we're straight off to the hall to meet the visitor with the pets. The man who'll let the owls fly round and the tarantulas crawl over my hand.

I sit on the carpet. I look at the red scratch marks on my hand. I stare down. If I look up, I might catch his eye, and he'll say, "Now, you can help me with this big snake – come out here." I keep looking down. All the classes are in the hall now. The mumbles of excitement stop as our headteacher says, "Here today, with some wonderful furred and feathered friends, is Mr Sutherland."

As soon as Mr Sutherland speaks, I recognize the Scottish voice. I jerk my head up in surprise and look straight into his eyes. We stare at each other. We know each other. He smiles and walks towards me. When he says, "Come here," my feet obey him, and I'm standing in front of two hundred children. It's so quiet, all I can hear is my heart banging just below my throat. Can't everyone hear it thump? I'm sure they can.

The man takes my scratched hand. I hear some of his words jumbling together. "On my way here today… child on a roof… old lady pointing… terrified cat stuck… brave young person here… scratched but determined to rescue it… wonderful… a really brave soul… round of applause, please."

There's the growing wave of sound, claps, cheers. And I think, That's not for the netball team or the Good Work kids, that's for me. I find myself smiling broadly. I can pick out faces, really friendly faces, nice faces. The Farrells are grinning, and the Armstrong twins are jerking their thumbs up, and Martin Lunch-box is smiling at me… Everybody is looking at me, and do you know what? I feel GREAT.

The twins and the Farrells walk home with me. We pass Mrs Stewart's house. She's leaning on her brush, looking up the road as usual. She looks at me as if she's met me in a dream once, and half smiles, half nods. Her cat is weaving around her ankles.

"That's Snowy," I say, and the Farrells laugh. Everyone will still call me Snowy, but not in a nasty way any more.

Oh, I still worry about the baths and spellings and the big loud Juniors in year six, but the day I rescued Snowy made me feel that I was just a little bit special and quite brave, and it made me feel braver and better about myself. I'm proud they call me Snowy now!

John Nevinson

'Snowy' © 1998 John Nevinson appears in STORY OF THE YEAR 6 published by Scholastic Ltd. Reproduced by permission of the publisher.

Friendly games

Are you ready for the Commonwealth Games? Have a go at these great ideas. Challenge your friends to see who's a medal winner.

Get into the spirit

Don't wear jewellery. ✦ Tie back long hair. ✦ Make sure there is plenty of space for all the activities. ✦ Wear trainers and loose comfy clothing.

Top tips

Don't try these activities if your back or knees hurt. ✦ Stop if an exercise hurts. ✦ Try not to tense up. ✦ Always stand upright and look forwards or where you are going. ✦ Remember to keep breathing! ✦ These activities are best done outside.

Warm up and cool off

Take a look at page 68 for the best way of warming up and cooling down before and after exercise.

Discus

Stand behind the line. Throw a paper plate as far as you can. Mark the spot where it first touches the ground. Try it with a frisbee, if you have one. Which one was easier to throw?

Shot putt

Stand behind the line. From your shoulder throw a ball as far as you can. Mark the spot where it first hits the ground. Who can throw it furthest? Try throwing balls of different size and weight.

Bowls

Put a baked bean tin 20 paces from your start line. Throw a ball aiming to get it as close to the tin as you can. Who can get the closest? Let each person have three tries.

Photographs by Diana Aynaci

On the beam

Mark a chalk line on the ground. Try walking along it without wobbling. Now try hopping along the line. Who can get from one end to the other without falling off?

Rolling

Crouch down with your hands stretched out in front. Roll forward onto the palms of your hands, then tumble your body over. Try to go straight. How many can you do in a row? Can you roll backwards?

Don't do this exercise on a hard surface.

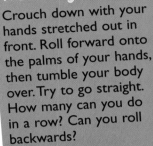

Up and down relay

Mark two chalk lines about 40 steps apart. Split into teams, each with the same number of runners. Half of each team stands at each line. The first person in each team runs to the other line and hands over a bean bag to her team mate who then runs back. The bean bag is handed on and the runners keep going until everyone has run. Which team was first over the finish line?

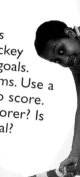

Hockey

Roll up and tape some newspapers to make your hockey sticks. Mark two goals. Split into two teams. Use a soft ball and try to score. Who is the ace scorer? Is anyone good in goal?

Long jump

Stand behind the line with both feet together. Jump as far as you can. Remember to bend both knees as you land.

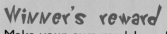

Winner's reward

Make your own medals and hold a ceremony to present them. Have gold, silver and bronze awards for each event. Also give medals to whoever tried the hardest and was the best team player.

Find out more about the 2002 Commonwealth Games on page 34.

Go for it Guides!

Get yourself ready to be a Guide by finding out the facts about what they get up to.

Warm welcome
Guides are really friendly and will give you a great welcome. Most new Guides get a special welcome pack that's crammed with goodies and information.

New friends
You'll soon become part of a Patrol, which is four to eight Guides. They'll have picked a name for themselves, so you could be a dolphin, a penguin or a panda. Some of them wear a metal pin badge to show what Patrol they are in.

Guide wear
Guides wear some really trendy clothes. They choose from a range of items that look so good you'll want to wear them all the time.

GuideLines
You'll need to sign the Guide unit's guidelines. This is a code that everyone in the unit has made up and agreed to keep. It covers all the things they think really matter, like being nice to each other, remembering to clean up, or maybe even having chocolate treats.

Guide photographs by Kelvin Rogers: Brownie photograph by Moose Azim.

G file and G card

Guides have a great personal organiser called the *G file*. It is full of information you need to know about being a Guide. There's space for making a note of everything you get up to at Guides, as well as having a year planner and stickers. There is also room to keep your *G card* which is your special Guide unit membership card.

Go for it!

Patrols pick what they want to do from Go For It! activity packs. Everyone in the Patrol gets a say. One week it could be cooking, next having a de-stress evening, and after that you could have a real party. When you've done a Go For It! you get a special card to keep in your *G file*.

Challenges and badges

Guides have got plenty of challenges and badges, just like Brownies. The *G file* contains details of what you need to do. Just in case you do run out, or fancy an extra challenge, your Guider has information about plenty of other badges you can try.

Getting away

Guides love going to camp or away on holiday. Sometimes it's for a weekend or it could be for a week. There is also the great Guide sleepover which you can organise yourself. You could even get the chance to go abroad, or meet Guides from other countries at camps in the UK.

Visit www.guides.org.uk and look at members, for lots more information, or phone 0800 1695901.

29

Eating gold

Have a go at these yellow and golden food ideas. They're perfect for a jubilee party.

Top tips
Ask an adult to help you in the kitchen. ❀ Always wash your hands before cooking. ❀ Tie back long hair.

Egg layer

Ingredients
1 hard-boiled egg ★ 1 tomato ★ some lettuce leaves or other green salad ★ 2 slices of granary bread ★ margarine ★ mayonnaise

You need
egg slicer (optional) ★ sharp knife ★ chopping board ★ clean, dry tea towel ★ knife

1 Slice the egg using the egg slicer or sharp knife. Slice the tomato.

2 Separate some lettuce leaves. Cut off the thick stalks. Rinse the leaves, then pat them dry.

3 Spread both slices of bread with margarine. Add a thin layer of mayonnaise to one slice.

4 Arrange the egg and tomato slices. Balance the lettuce on top. Add the other slice of bread. Carefully cut in half diagonally.

Try this
Instead of slicing the egg, mash it with some mayonnaise. Fork it onto the bread then cover with a layer of tomatoes and lettuce.

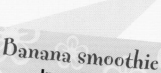

Lemon aid

Ingredients

2 lemons ❈ 2 teaspoonfuls honey ❈ 1 litre fizzy water ❈ ice cubes

You need

sharp knife ❈ chopping board ❈ lemon squeezer ❈ jug ❈ whisk or fork ❈ plastic food wrap

Banana smoothie

Ingredients

550ml (1 pint) milk ❈ 4 scoops vanilla ice-cream ❈ 1 banana

You need

bowl and whisk, or a foodmixer ❈ fork ❈ bowl ❈ glasses and straws

1 Cut one lemon in half and squeeze it. Pour the juice into the jug. Add the honey.

1 Mix the ice-cream and milk in the bowl, or whizz in the foodmixer for about 30 seconds.

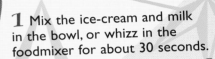

2 Wash the other lemon. Cut it into segments or slices.

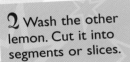

2 Mash the banana. Add to the milk mix. Whisk again.

3 Add the water to the jug and mix well. Add the lemon segments. Cover with food wrap and stand it in the fridge for 30 minutes. Serve with ice cubes on a hot day.

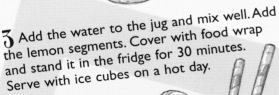

Have a go at these

Try some lemon jelly – really tasty with ice-cold cream. ❈ Make a fruit salad with yellow and pale green fruit, like yellow apples, seedless green grapes, melon, grapefruit and banana. ❈ Experiment with eggs, learn how to poach, boil, scramble and fry. ❈ Cook some custard pies. ❈ Tuck in to some macaroni cheese.

Japanese puzzles

Japan is one of the hosts of this year's football World Cup. Have a go at these mind-bending puzzles.

Get that word

See if you can find these Japanese words hidden in the square.

Tea ✓

Kobe
Rice
Silk

Chuka
Futon
Haiku
Kyoto
Lotus
Okane
Osaka
Sushi
Tokyo

Shinto

Emperor
Noodles

Buddhism
Fujiyama
Japanese

Computers

Electronics

```
K Y O T O N K C H U K A
F E L E C T R O N I C S
L M F U T O N M M M B O H
S P K F O K U P T U K I
H E J U S Y U U K D A N
A R L J R O H T O D N T
I O R I C E T E A H E O
K R S Y Y S A R S I L K
U O S A K A E S I S K O
T I A M S U S H I M O K
J A P A N E S E C N B O
L O T U S N O O D L E S
```

Same word

Match these characters into pairs.
Find the one that appears three times.

Illustrated by John Haslam

Pairs of sticks

Match the chopsticks into pairs. Which is the odd one out?

Noodled out

Whose noodle has run out?

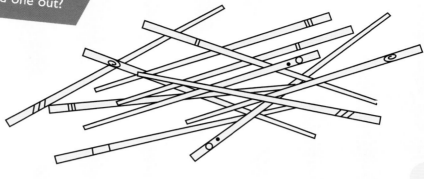

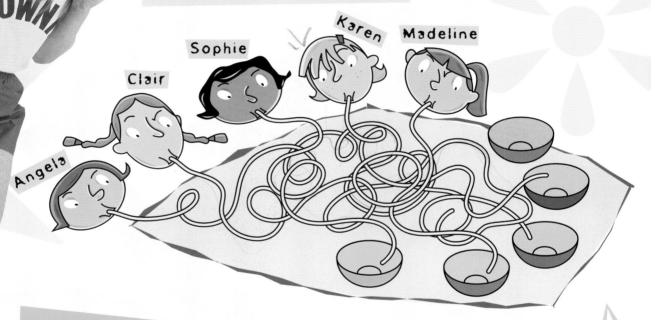

Clair
Sophie
Karen
Madeline
Angela

Karaoke night

Find the names of the groups being performed at the karaoke competition.

Celeste

Steps   Britney   7

Mumba Child   Robbie

Destiny's   Hear   Craig

Street   Boys   Back

David   Samantha   S Club

Break   Spice   Spears   Westlife   'say

Point   Daphne and   Williams   Sugababes   Kitten

Girls   Atomic

How did you get on?
Check your answers
on page 76.

Host the games

This is a special year for Manchester as it hosts the 2002 Commonwealth Games. It is going to be the first Games of the new millennium and the biggest one ever.

Friendly games

The Commonwealth Games is also known as the Friendly Games. More than 5,000 athletes from 72 nations will be competing in it. Over a quarter of the world's population live in these countries. As a result, it's hoped that up to two billion people worldwide will be watching what happens.

Manchester

Manchester is sometimes called the capital of the north of England. More than two and a half million people live there.

Sporting city

Manchester is a city enthusiastic about sport. It is home to the world famous Manchester United Football Club which has its home at Old Trafford. At Old Trafford there is also an international cricket ground where many test matches are played. The National Cycling Centre in East Manchester is the fastest cycle track in the world. In 2003, Manchester City Football Club will move to the new City of Manchester Stadium which has been built specially for the Games. The stadium lies within Sportcity, a complex of sport venues in East Manchester.

Other sport spots

The Manchester Evening News Arena is the biggest indoor arena in Europe. ★ In 1996, Manchester was a regional centre for the European football championships Euro 96. ★ Manchester recently staged the Triathlon World Championships. ★ Manchester has its own basketball and ice-hockey teams.

The Commonwealth

The Commonwealth is an international association of nations, including the United Kingdom, that feel their friendship with each other is special. Queen Elizabeth II is welcomed in all the Commonwealth nations, so it is extra special that the Games are being hosted here in her Golden Jubilee year.

The Games

The Opening Ceremony is on 25 July 2002 with the first events on Friday 26 July. There is a huge range of sports from athletics, badminton, cycling, judo, netball and swimming to gymnastics, hockey, triathlon, rugby and weightlifting, plus many more. It's a lot to fit in by the time the Games end on 4 August.

Mascot

Kit is the official mascot of the Games. He first appeared back in 1998 at the end of the last Commonwealth Games held in Malaysia.

Friendship symbol

The Spirit of Friendship symbol shows three people on a winners' podium. Their arms are held high to show what it's like to win and celebrate. There are three reasons for the Games – sport, culture and friendship. That's why there are three people. The three colours also mean something. Red is for success and trying your best. Blue is for being reliable and confident. Green is for being loyal and giving.

Join in

As well as the actual Games, there is the Spirit of Friendship festival that will take place all over the UK. Plus specially for Brownies there's The Guide Association's Spirit of Friendship Award, with a badge and certificate for everyone who takes part. Log on to www.guides.org.uk to find out the latest information and what you need to do to join in.

Visit www.commonwealthgames.com for the latest news and information on the Games.

Bonsai petals

The Japanese grow tiny plants, called bonsai, and make ornamental gardens. Create your own mini indoor garden.

You need

plain card   scissors   tissue or crêpe paper in bright colours   green card   stapler   20 cocktail sticks   glue   colourful sticky spots   plasticine   tray   sand   small pebbles or cones (optional)   pencil

1 From the plain card cut three card templates. One small circle about 3cm in diameter. A medium one about 5cm and a large one about 7cm.

2 Use the templates to make about 40 each of the small, medium and large circles from the tissue paper.

3 Make a leaf template about 6cm tall. Use it to cut 20 leaf shapes from the green card.

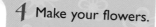

4 Make your flowers.

Place three small circles on top of a medium one. Staple them to a cocktail stick. Scrunch the middle circles, then the outer one.

Pick one circle of each size. Staple them to a cocktail stick. Cut towards the middle. Arrange the petals.

Cut wavy edges to four circles. Staple them to a cocktail stick. Pull the circles forward. Try cutting petal shapes.

5 Keep going until you have made 20 flowers. Stick a spot to the centre of each one. Glue a leaf to the back of each cocktail stick.

Glue

6 When the flowers are dry, stick each one in a blob of plasticine.

7 Fill the tray with sand. Make little holes where you want to place your flowers.

8 Stick the flowers in so the plasticine is just covered.

Give it a go!

Try making your own bonsai garden with real plants. ✳ Change your plants every few weeks or when you fancy new colours. ✳ Have a colour theme, like your favourite football team's colours.

9 Smooth the sand with your fingers. Position the pebbles and stones.

10 Make lines in the sand with the end of the pencil.

A helping hand

Jo's in a rush to get to Brownies.

What a day! George was sick so I left work early.

Oh, right.

I'm going to Brownies now.

My Mum seems really stressed, Rosie.

On the way to Brownies...

Nan's doing your tea, so pop in on your way home.

Okay.

Rosie's right! But what can I do? I'll speak to Nan about it.

It must be hard work looking after you and George. Plus she's at work all day.

After a great time at Brownies, Jo goes to her Nan's home for something to eat. Jo gets on really well with her Nan who always seems to have the right answer to Jo's problems.

Jo is worried about her Mum and wants to help. But what can she do? Can Nan help her find a solution?

At Nan's home...

Don't worry. I've got an idea!

The next day at school...

What did you get up to after Brownies?

I went round to my Nan's.

Did you speak to her about your Mum?

It's something I should have done a long time ago.

Yeah! Let me tell you about our brilliant plan.

Can I lend a hand, too?

Turn the page to find out what Jo and her Nan have planned.

When Jo's Mum is at work, Rosie, Jo and her Nan put their plan into action. They are going to clean the house, make the beds and cook dinner. Jo has also bought her Mum some flowers as a special present.

Hopefully, Jo's Mum will come in from work and sit down to relax. Will their plan work?

At Jo's home…

Let's start with George's toys.

I can't wait to see the surprise on your Mum's face!

Let's get this bed made.

I hope Mum likes these flowers.

I'll be careful not to knock them over!

Phew! That was hard work. No wonder Mum's tired all the time.

40

41

Commonwealth capers

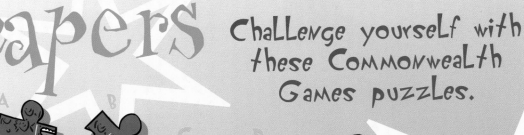

Challenge yourself with these Commonwealth Games puzzles.

Make the gymnast

Which missing piece will complete the puzzle?

Longest jump

Who jumped the furthest?

Javelin spotting

Spot the two javelins that are the same.

Cross country

Find the right way round the cross-country trail.

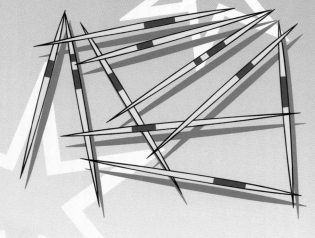

Join them up

Match the first half of a sporty word on the left with its end on the right.

shot	jump
triple	event
track	country
cross	putt
lawn	bowls
table	biking
mountain	lifting
weight	tennis

Hit the jack

Who hit the jack at bowls?

jack

Country search

Find these Commonwealth countries in the square.

Fiji

Ghana
India
Malta

Canada
Tuvalu

Zambia

Jamaica
Nigeria
St Lucia

Anguilla
Malaysia
Tanzania

Australia
Gibraltar
Singapore

Bangladesh
Montserrat
New Zealand

```
C O M G I B R A L T A R
M S J A M A I C A M O A
T I C A N A D A B O N N
A N E W Z E A L A N D G
N G F I J I U G N T S U
Z A M B I A S H G S T I
A P W M A L T A L E L L
N O E A L T R N A R U L
I R I N D I A A D R C A
A E T U V A L U E A I H
M A L A Y S I A S T A G
N I G E R I A A H M E S
```

Starting at the top left corner, put the spare letters in the squares below.

[ ] [ ] [ ] [ ] [ ] [ ] [ ] [ ] [ ] [ ] [ ] [ ]

[ ] [ ] [ ] [ ] [ ]

Are you a winner? Go to page 76 to find out.

Lily pad life?

Get the fascinating facts about frogs in the UK and round the world.

Frogs galore

Frogs come in all shapes, sizes and colours. Some live in trees, others in swamps or pond water. Some even burrow underground. Frogs are amphibians which means they live both in the water and on land. The common frog can be found all over the UK. Take a look at how it grows and lives.

Spawn

The frog starts life as a tiny egg laid in the water. All the eggs stick together and are called spawn. The black dot will become the tadpole, but many don't make it to this stage as the spawn gets eaten by fish and other creatures.

Hatching

The tadpole gets bigger and pushes out of the egg. It hangs to the outside of the spawn until its tail is strong enough for it to swim. At the side of the tadpole's head, feathery gills grow so it can get oxygen from the water.

Growing up

The tadpole eats tiny plants and grows quickly. By the time it is five weeks old, the back legs can be seen. Next the tadpole's lungs grow and gills disappear, so it has to go to the water's surface to breathe. The tadpole's colour starts to change to mottled brown.

All change

Over the next seven weeks, front legs begin to grow where the gills were. The tadpole still needs its long tail for swimming though. As well as eating plants, the tadpole begins to eat water fleas and other small insects.

Almost a frog

By 12 weeks the tadpole is almost a frog. Its tail is getting shorter and it uses the webbed feet on its back legs to swim. These strong back legs will later help it jump on dry land. Next it loses its tail totally and starts to clamber out of the water. It learns to listen for danger and hide under stones and leaves.

Adult frog

By the time it is three months old, the frog is eating more insects. It has learned to use its long sticky tongue to catch them. After two years the frog goes back to where it was born to lay its own eggs and start the cycle again.

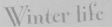

Winter life

During winter, the frog hibernates in a hole in the bank. This means it sleeps through the cold winter months and wakes up again when the weather gets warm in the spring.

Tree frogs

There are some tree frogs that never live on the ground. Instead of webbed feet they have sticky toes for climbing. Some can even climb up glass.

Frog facts

A frog can breathe through its skin as well as its mouth. ★ A frog's skin is very delicate and must not dry out. ★ A frog can live for up to 10 years. ★ A frog can jump over three metres. ★ When some male frogs croak, a sack of skin under their chin blows up like a balloon.

Underground

Some frogs burrow underground to keep cool, stay out of danger or to make sure they don't dry out.

World frogs

The Goliath frog, found in Africa, is large enough to eat small birds and mice. ★ In Australia, White's tree frogs make their home in people's bathrooms. ★ The blue tree frog from South America has poisonous skin.

All photographs supplied by Oxford Scientific Films: background leaf frog perched on plant, blue poison dart frog and painted reed frog croaking Michael Fogden; frog spawn London Scientific Films: front legs forming and tail reabsorption G I Bernard: tadpole gills and leaping frog Michael Leach.

Round recipes

Wondering what to munch when watching the big match? These mouth-watering treats are just what you need.

Football bites

Ingredients
75g icing sugar ★ 35g cocoa powder ★ extra icing sugar and cocoa powder for sprinkling ★ 75g crushed digestive biscuits ★ 75g soft cheese ★ dark and white chocolate drops (optional)

You need
mixing bowl ★ sieve ★ 3 large plates ★ spoon ★ plastic food wrap

1 Sift the icing sugar and cocoa powder. Mix in the cheese until it's smooth.

2 Mix in the crushed biscuits. Cover with food wrap. Leave in the fridge for 30 minutes.

3 Shape the mixture into 25 balls. Cover 16 in icing sugar and nine in cocoa powder.

4 Arrange them in a circle like this to look like a football.

Try making larger balls. Decorate them to look like footballs using white or dark chocolate drops.

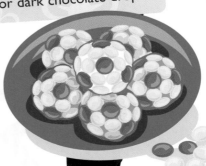

Illustrated by Tim Kahane

Meat balls

Ingredients
1 small onion ★ 450g minced meat ★ salt and pepper ★ 50g cheese ★ 1 egg ★ 2 tablespoons vegetable oil

You need
sharp knife ★ chopping board ★ 2 mixing bowls ★ cheese grater ★ fork ★ spoon ★ frying pan ★ fish slice

Fairy fans

Ingredients
fairy cakes ★ icing sugar ★ food colouring ★ water

You need
mixing bowl ★ spoon

Mix the icing sugar, food colouring and water. Cover the fairy cakes. Try making two or three different colours and icing the cakes in stripes or a pattern.

1 Peel the onion and chop it finely. Add it to the minced meat. Add a little salt and pepper.

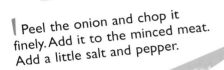

2 Grate the cheese. Beat the egg. Add them to the mince. Mix well.

3 Heat the oil in the frying pan. Divide the mixture into four balls. Place each one in the frying pan.

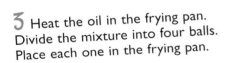

4 Fry for about ten minutes, turning them from time to time, until cooked through.

Serve with some crunchy salad, full of radishes and cherry tomatoes!

Great competition!

Fancy making your own
jewellery, creating scented soaps
or transforming your room?
How would you like your own
camera, personal CD-player
or two-way radio?

The prizes

There are ten great prizes of these three books that
are packed with fantastic ideas for every girl. Two
lucky winners will also get a £40 voucher to spend
at any Dixons, Currys, The Link or PC World store.
You can choose from a great range of the latest
gadgets like the camera above and the sound
systems on the next page.

crafty girl
beauty
things to make and do

by Jennifer Traig
and Julianne

A fabulous guide to
becoming healthy from
the inside out.

Includes over 500 beads and enough material for 10 projects

bead ❀ girl
25 Sparkly Beading Projects
from Tiaras to Toe Rings

by
Mikyla Bruder
&
Photographs by
David Magnusson

crafty girl
cool stuff
things to make and do

glue

Traig
anne Balmain

Stunning ideas to
personalise the ordinary
and create your own space.

Not just full of great
ideas but it contains all
you need to get started.

**If you just can't wait to get your hands on these great books you can get copies by phoning 01206 255800. As a special
offer to B◯◯◯◯ *Annual 2002* readers there is no postage charge. Get an adult you know to do this for you.**

How to be a winner

Draw a picture of your dream bedroom. Don't forget to show how you would personalise it. What kind of bed would you have… where would you keep your jewellery… think about how you can make boring bins and cupboards more exciting… would you have the latest sounds being played?

What you need to do

1 Draw your fantastic entry.

2 On the back write:
✪ your name.
✪ your age.
✪ your address.
✪ your favourite three things from this Annual.
✪ the best thing about being a Brownie.

3 Put your entry in an envelope to:
Brownie Annual 2002
Dixons and Chronicle Books Competition
The Guide Association
17–19 Buckingham Palace Road
London
SW1W 0PT

4 Don't forget a stamp. Then pop it in a letter box.

Hurry! The closing date is 31 January 2002.

49

Guinea pig pets

Whether you already have one, or want to get one, you're sure to find some top tips for looking after a pet guinea pig here.

Where are they from?

Guinea pigs are popular pet rodents because they are easy to tame. Their proper name is cavies, and originally they came from South America. In the wild they live in grassland and like to burrow in the undergrowth.

Long or short?

There are many types of guinea pig. The main difference is the length of their hair. Long-haired guinea pigs must be groomed every day, while short-haired ones need grooming at least once a week. Always brush in the direction its fur grows.

Living together

Guinea pigs are social animals and live together in large family groups. It is unfair to keep a single guinea pig as a pet. An all-female group is best, as two males will usually fight and a mixed group breeds quickly.

Picking up

Guinea pigs should be handled every day. Before picking one up, make sure it can see you. Hold it gently but firmly with both hands making sure its bottom is supported. Be careful not to drop the guinea pig.

Living in or out

A rabbit hutch with a ramp in an enclosure makes a good home. Raise it off the ground so it doesn't get damp. Cover the enclosure with wire mesh if there are other animals about. Guinea pigs kept outside in the summer need to be moved indoors when the weather gets colder. Guinea pigs don't like draughts, damp or cold.

Happy home

Guinea pigs need living space and a sleeping area. These should be cleaned at least once a week, or more often if they are wet or dirty. In cold weather put in extra bedding, but make sure air can get in. In the living area they like little hidey-holes and branches.

Exercise

Guinea pigs need quite a lot of exercise. They like to roam and should not be shut in a hutch for a long time.

Food and water

As well as fresh grass, make sure they always have a supply of fresh hay, grains and vegetables. Put hay in a container so it isn't trampled. Cut vegetables into chunks. Give a small amount of grains, like wholemeal bread or oats, twice a day. Clean out food bowls every time you feed them. Leave enough food to last overnight. Use a drip bottle for water that they can easily reach. Keep it clean and full of fresh water.

Grazing animals

Wild guinea pigs graze and live on stems, leaves and seeds. A guinea pig pen can be moved round the lawn, but be careful to avoid areas that may have been sprayed with chemicals.

Gnaw

Guinea pigs need wood to gnaw on so their front teeth don't grow too long. It is best if the wood is fairly hard and still has bark on it.

Care

Be careful picking up a guinea pig that doesn't know you. ❖ Get someone to look after your guinea pigs every day when you are on holiday. Ask that they are kept clean, well-fed, groomed and exercised. ❖ Wash your hands before and after feeding or handling any pet.

Health

Guinea pigs live about four to seven years. ❖ Guinea pigs can catch colds from humans. ❖ A vet needs to trim a guinea pig's front teeth and claws if they are too long. ❖ Every day check a guinea pig's eyes, ears, nose, skin and fur to make sure they are healthy.

Background Dutch guinea pig and long-coated guinea pig RSPCA/t A Janes: girl holding guinea pig, two guinea pigs eating and hutch RSPCA/Angela Hampton: guinea pig on straw RSPCA/Andrew Forsyth: guinea pig eating Oxford Scientific Films/Zig Leszczynski.

Football facts

During 2002 the World Cup finals will be played. Find out some facts behind the world's most popular sport.

The World Cup

This is football's most prized competition. The finals are held every four years. The hosts of the 2002 World Cup are Japan and Korea. It is a massive international event making the winners the best football team in the world.

Winners

In 1930, the first World Cup finals were hosted by Uruguay in South America. Uruguay won in a final match against Argentina. The winners of the last World Cup in 1998 were France, who also hosted the event. Brazil has won the World Cup four times. Germany and Italy have each won it three times.

FIFA

The World Cup is organised by FIFA, which stands for the Fédération Internationale de Football Association. FIFA was set up in 1904 and to start with only had seven members – Belgium, Denmark, France, Holland, Spain, Sweden and Switzerland.

Playing fair

The rules for the World Cup are decided by FIFA as every country has slight differences in their rules. In the 1998 World Cup, a total of 643 games were played throughout the tournament, so it was important that the same rules were followed by everyone.

Getting there

More than 160 countries take part in the World Cup, but only 32 countries compete in the finals. Every country that makes it to the finals gets there by playing a series of qualifying games about a year in advance. Countries are grouped together, and the best teams from each group go to the finals.

Football start

It is hard to tell when football was first played. Over 2,200 years ago the Chinese played a game like it. Ancient Greeks and Romans also played games like football, but to us today they probably looked more like rugby. The Romans may have brought their version of football to Britain about 1,800 years ago.

Modern football

In 1863 the first football association in the world was founded in England. It established a set of rules for all the teams to play by.

Match facts

A game of football lasts 90 minutes. Extra time is added to make up for stops during the game, like players being injured. ✤ Each team has 11 players and two substitute players. ✤ For a goal to be scored the ball must completely cross the goal line. ✤ A football must be 68 to 71 centimetres round. ✤ A football pitch is 90 to 120 metres long and 64 to 75 metres wide.

In the past...

It was in 1890 that nets behind the goalposts were first used. ✤ In 1314 the Lord Mayor of London banned football as it was getting too rowdy. ✤ Mob football was played up and down high streets and everyone in the town or village took part.

Women footballers

Women were definitely playing football over 500 years ago, maybe even before that. The first match that was recorded was held in 1895, and there was an international game in 1920. Crowds of up to 53,000 watched women's football at the start of the last century. The first women's World Cup was held China in 1991, and the USA won.

Stolen Cup

In 1966 the World Cup trophy was stolen in London. Fortunately a dog called Pickles found it with his owner when they were out walking. The trophy was given to Brazil to keep in 1970 when a new one was made, but in 1983 it was stolen again and has never been found.

Get involved

Women's football is one of the fastest growing sports in this country. If you want to find out more, including how to get involved visit:
www.the-fa.org
www.scottishfa.co.uk
www.faw.org.uk
www.fai.ie
Go to www.fifaworldcup.co.uk for more World Cup information.

Weather

This colourful mobile is great hung up outside. Or use it to brighten up your bedroom.

You need

2 wire coathangers * strong sticky tape * 4 pieces thin shiny card, 15cm x 15cm * ruler * pencil * hole punch * scissors * 4 brass paper fasteners * 20 foil pastry cases * darning needle * 1m thin string * 8 pieces ribbon, 30cm long

1 Put the coathangers into a cross shape. Tape the tops together and where they meet in the middle. Bend the hooks together and tape over them.

2 On the back of the shiny card draw faint lines joining the corners. Mark the points 1cm from the centre.

3 Make a small hole in each of the corners with the hole punch.

4 Cut along the pencil lines to the 1cm mark. Use the hole punch to make a small hole in the centre.

5 Carefully bend each corner into the centre without creasing or folding the card.

Illustrated by Stephanie Strickland

54

mobile

6 Put the paper fastener through each corner hole, then the centre one. Next attach it to one corner of the coathangers. Pinch the ends to make it secure.

7 Repeat this with the other three pieces of card.

8 Make a hole in the middle of each foil case. Cut the thin string into four equal lengths.

9 Tie a knot in one end of a piece of string. Thread it through one of the pastry cases. Tie another knot about 5cm above the first. Thread on another case then tie the next knot. Keep going until there are five cases in place.

10 Thread each piece of string with five cases. Tie each string to the arm of the coathangers. Then tie two ribbons to each arm.

Design your own

Personalise your mobile for your bedroom. ✿ Use pictures of your favourite stars and friends stuck to card. ✿ Cover all the wire with shiny tape. ✿ Hang big bright beads or glittery baubles from it for extra sparkle.

Use some strong string to tie your mobile somewhere that the wind can blow it. Watch it spin.

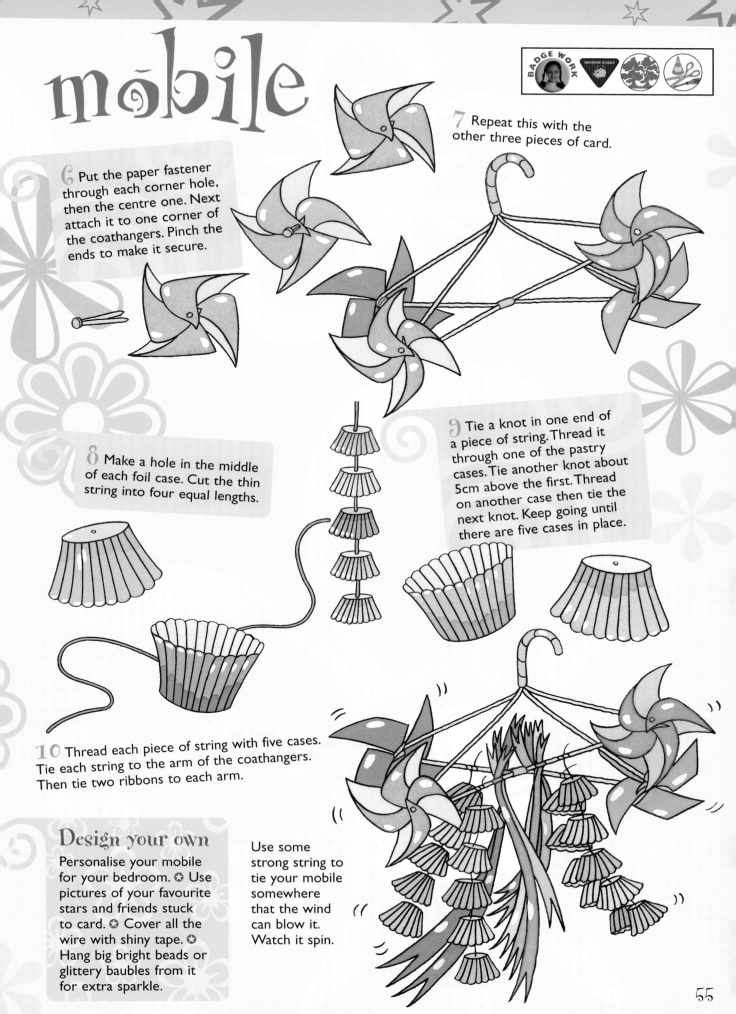

55

Caterpillar

Brown and furry
Caterpillar in a hurry,
Take your walk
To the shady leaf, or stalk,
Or what not,
Which may be the chosen spot.
No toad spy you,
Hovering bird of prey pass by you;
Spin and die,
To live again a butterfly.

Christina Rossetti

Illustrated by Beccy Blake

Get into Guides

These exciting puzzles will help you find your way round being a Guide.

On the clothes
Guides have their own trendy clothes label. Two of these are the right ones. Can you find them?

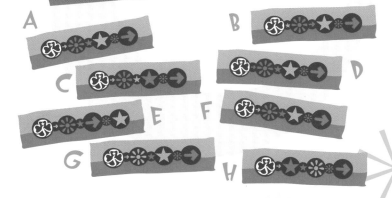

A
B
C
D
E F
G
H

On the trail
The Daffodil Patrol are out on a night hike. Can you help them get home?

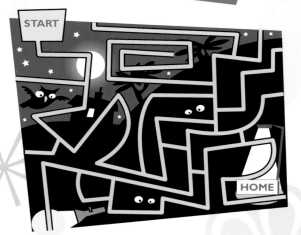

Holiday packing
Katie and Jamilla are packing for holiday. Spot the differences in what they are taking.

Katie

Jamilla

Illustrated by John Haslam

Muddled up

These Patrol names have got all muddled.
Can you sort them out?

NDLIPOH
FIAOLFDD
EIGPNNU
LHTTSIE
OSRE

Helping out

These Guides thought they'd clean their meeting place. Who has remembered to plug in?

Zoe   Fran

Anna   Imogen   Madison

Coded info

The Lion Patrol are using a special code to send messages to each other. Can you work them out?

G	M	S	Y	A	N	H	Z	T	B	I	O	U
A	B	C	D	E	F	G	H	I	J	K	L	M

C	P	J	V	D	Q	K	W	E	R	L	X	F
N	O	P	Q	R	S	T	U	V	W	X	Y	Z

Hint: BROWNIES would be spelt MDPRCTAQ using the secret cypher.

Ra'da hptch sgujtch calk raai.

Hwtyaq gda hdagk!

Oak'q zgea g jgdkx.

Ogqk raai'q ngqztpc qzpr rgq alsaooack.

Pegged out

The Guides can't find their tent pegs. Can you spot them?

Have you got what it takes?
Check page 76 for answers.

59

Jubilee year

It is a special year for one of The Guide Association's Patrons. Queen Elizabeth II will be celebrating her Golden Jubilee.

Royal family

Queen Elizabeth was born at 3am on 21 April 1926 at 17 Bruton Street, London. In 1947, when she was still Princess Elizabeth, she married Philip Mountbatten, who you may know better as Prince Philip or the Duke of Edinburgh. They have four children – Prince Charles, Princess Anne, Prince Andrew and Prince Edward – as well as six grandchildren.

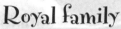

The Guide Association's badge decorated the top tier of Princess Elizabeth's wedding cake.

Becoming Queen

The Golden Jubilee is a celebration of when Princess Elizabeth ascended to the throne. She was proclaimed the new sovereign on 6 February 1952 following the death of her father King George VI. On 2 June 1953 the Coronation took place in Westminster Abbey in London. It is a ceremony full of traditional rituals that have developed over a thousand years.

Birthdays

The Queen has two birthdays. One is to celebrate the actual day she was born, and the other is an official date so more public celebrations can take place. The Queen's official birthday is always celebrated in June when she takes part in Trooping the Colour.

Royal Patron

Both Queen Elizabeth II and Queen Elizabeth, The Queen Mother are Patrons of The Guide Association. Queen Elizabeth's younger sister Princess Margaret is the Association's President.

Association links

The Guide Association has had many links with the Royal family. Guides were set up at Buckingham Palace. The young Princess Elizabeth was a Guide and became the Patrol Leader for the Swallow Patrol. She went on to be the Chief Ranger in 1946. In 1952 she became our Patron.

Royal members

Princess Margaret was a keen Brownie in the Leprechaun Six. She went on to become the Association's President in 1965. Both her daughter and the Queen's daughter, Princess Anne, were Brownies.

Golden Jubilee

The word 'jubilee' comes from 'jubilate' which means shout for joy and be glad. Gold is the colour associated with celebrations involving 50, like wedding anniversaries.

Celebration!

For the Queen's Coronation Brownies and Guides all over the Commonwealth held a special three month tribute and sent messages to congratulate the Queen. In 1977, for the Queen's Silver Jubilee, Brownies and Guides everywhere took part in celebrations and wore a special badge. The Golden Jubilee will be a special year again, and another badge will be available from The Guide Association.

The Commonwealth

The Queen is the head of the Commonwealth, so it is even more special that the 2002 Commonwealth Games is being held in Manchester. The Queen regularly travels to other Commonwealth countries where she is always made welcome. Turn to page 34 for details on the 2002 Games.

Travel

The Queen travels all over the world building links with other countries on behalf of the UK. She is the only person in the country who can travel abroad without a passport.

Animal lover

The Queen is well known for liking animals and has several corgi dogs. She is also very keen on horses.

Busy life

The Queen gets about 1,000 invitations each year and more than 250 letters a day. She carries out over 450 engagements like state events and visiting schools, hospitals and factories.

Find out more

Find out more about the Queen, her work and the Golden Jubilee at www.royal.gov.uk and how Brownies can join in the celebrations at www.guides.org.uk.

Commonwealth cuisine

Have a go at these tasty snacks from Commonwealth countries.

Australian pavlova

Ingredients

5 eggs ★ 150g caster sugar
250ml double cream
350g creamy yoghurt ★ small
can pineapple chunks

You need

baking tray ★ rice paper ★ plate
★ pencil ★ mixing bowl ★
whisk ★ spoon ★ oven gloves

1 Pre-heat the oven to 150°C/gas mark 2. Mark a circle on the rice paper.

Top tips

Ask an adult to help you in the kitchen. ✦ Always wash your hands before cooking. ✦ Tie back long hair.

2 Crack the eggs and separate the yolks from the whites.

3 Whisk the whites until they are stiff and make peaks.

4 Add one tablespoon of sugar. Whisk well. Add another one and whisk again. Keep going until all the sugar is gone.

5 Spoon the mixture inside the circle. Bake for five minutes. Lower the temperature to 120°C/gas mark ½. Bake for 50 minutes until it is crisp. Leave it to cool.

6 Rinse the bowl then whisk the cream until it's thick. Mix in the yoghurt.

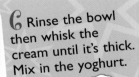

7 Pile the cream in the middle. Arrange the pineapple chunks.

Indian parathas

Ingredients
½ tablespoon oil plus extra for frying ❖ ½ tablespoon butter ❖ 25g mint (fresh is best) ❖ ½ teaspoon cumin powder ❖ ¼ teaspoon mild chilli powder ❖ 1 teaspoon salt ❖ 1 teaspoon lemon juice ❖ 100ml water ❖ 300g plain flour

You need
frying pan ❖ wooden spoon ❖ blender or whisk ❖ sieve ❖ mixing bowl ❖ rolling pin ❖ fish slice

1 Heat the oil and butter in the pan until melted. Leave it to cool.

2 Blend the mint, cumin, chilli powder, salt, water and lemon juice for a few seconds.

3 Sieve the flour. Mix in the oil and mint mixtures to make a stretchy dough.

4 Sprinkle some flour on your work surface. Make eight balls from the dough.

5 Roll each ball until it's 10cm round.

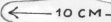

← 10 CM →

6 Heat some oil in the pan over a low heat. Cook each side of the parathas until they are light brown.

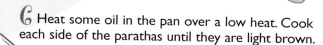

Kenyan baked bananas

Ingredients
4 bananas ❖ 2 tablespoons brown sugar ❖ 1 teaspoon cinnamon ❖ 30g margarine

You need
knife ❖ ovenproof dish ❖ pan ❖ spoon ❖ cooking foil ❖ oven gloves

1 Pre-heat the oven to 180°C/gas mark 4. Cut the bananas in half and place in the dish.

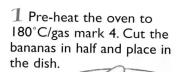

2 Melt the butter on a low heat. Stir in the sugar and cinnamon.

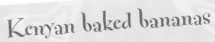

3 Pour the mixture over the bananas. Cover with foil. Bake for 50 minutes.

63

Super Brownie

Super Brownie's new friend

Next week a new Brownie is joining us. I know you'll all make her feel welcome but I'd like one of you to be her special friend.

Who?

I'm going to pull one of your names from this hat.

The best buddy will be... Laura!

Yeah!

The following week...

This is Zoe, everyone.

Hi, Zoe!

Hi, I'm Laura. I'm going to help you settle in.

H... hello.

Turn the page to find out how Super Brownie helps Zoe even more.

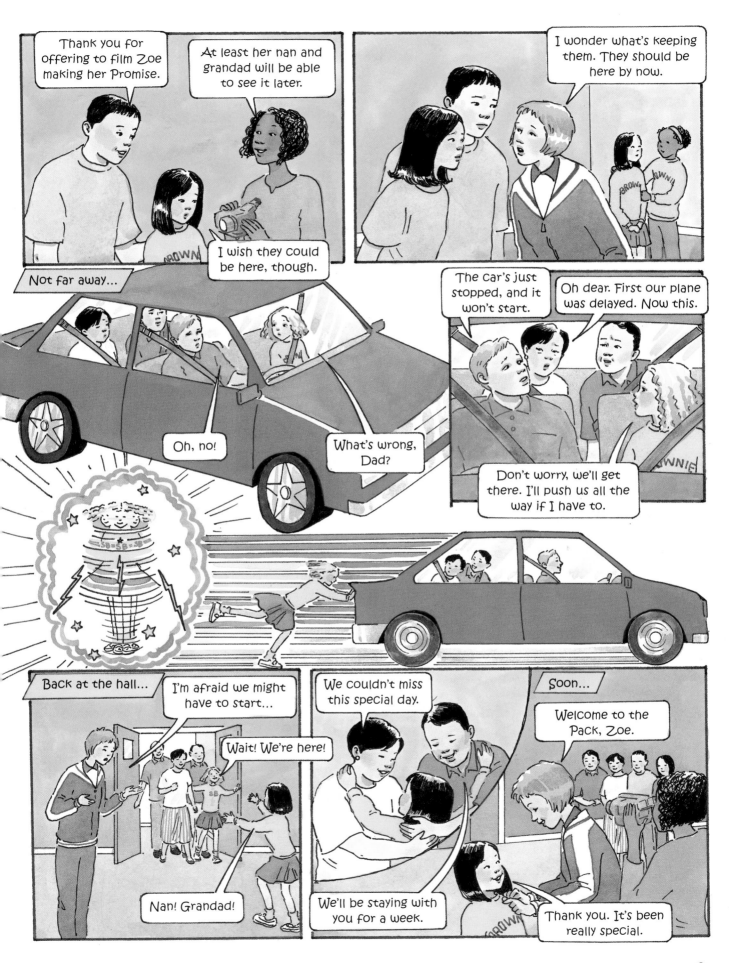

On your marks

Being fit and supple can help you play games well. Get ready for a summer of sport with these exercises.

Warm up

Stretch up as if reaching for the stars. ✪ March on the spot swinging your arms back and forwards.

Get set

Don't wear jewellery. ✦ Tie back long hair. ✦ Make sure there is plenty of space for all the activities. ✦ Wear trainers and loose comfy clothing.

Skipping

Skip as fast as you can. How many can you manage? Have a go at skipping backwards or hopping instead of jumping.

Lunges

Take a big step forward with your right foot. Keep your hands on your hips. Push forward and down to stretch your left leg. Try it again with your left foot forward.

Stretching

With your feet apart stretch to your right. Don't lean back or forwards. Can your fingers touch the side of your knees? Now stretch to your left.

Thrown in

Hold a ball above your head. Lean back as far as you can. If you are outside, throw the ball at a target. How close did you get to your mark?

CycLing

Lie on your back with your hands flat on the ground. Lift up your legs and pedal round and round. Try not to wobble. Have a go at pedalling backwards.

Don't do this exercise on a hard surface.

Step up

Find a solid step. Step up with your right foot then your left. Step down with you right foot first. Do ten step ups, then try again using your left foot first.

Toe touches

Keep your feet together and knees straight. Bend over and try to touch your toes.

Dribble

Practise running and kicking a ball at the same time. Go slowly and don't kick the ball too hard. Try to go in a straight line to begin with. Then see if you can go round corners.

CooL down

Stretch again as high as you can. ✪ Stand straight and roll your head. ✪ Relax and shrug your shoulders. ✪ Shake your arms down to your finger tips. ✪ Shake out each leg. ✪ Put on a sweatshirt before you get cold.

How weLL did you do?

Practise all the exercises. Then have a go at each one to see how many you can do without stopping. Keep a record here.
- ☐ Lunges
- ☐ Skipping
- ☐ Stretching
- ☐ Throw in
- ☐ Cycling
- ☐ Step up
- ☐ Toe touches
- ☐ Dribble

Top tips

Don't try these activities if your back or knees hurt. ✦ Stop if an exercise hurts. ✦ Always stand upright and look forwards or where you are going. ✦ Try not to tense up. ✦ Remember to keep breathing!

A special Brownie

Miss Dorothy Com is an extraordinary Brownie. Find out all about her and where you can visit her.

Fact file

Real name	Dorothy Com, or Dot Com to her friends
Age	9
Lives	with her mum and dad who are called Susie and Bill Com
Pets	a dog called Wizard
Best friend	Genie
Hobbies	reading, listening to music, swimming and, of course, being a Brownie
Special feature	Dot can travel the internet and has adventures in cyber space!

How it started

Dot Com is just like any other nine-year-old Brownie. She enjoys all the things Brownies have fun doing but Dot has a very special talent. One day, when she was using her Dad's laptop computer, Dot was literally sucked into the computer's screen and out onto the super highway of the internet!

Dot's travels

Dot soon realised that she could visit lots of great sites, just like www.guides.org.uk where you can find out all the fun of being a Brownie. She knows about being safe on the internet as well. You can join Dot in her fabulous world of cyber space and read her adventures on line three times a week by visiting her website.

Dot's website

Being such an internet traveller, Dot has her own website. There's lots to see and do if you visit it. ✤ Dot's daily diary has got all the latest on what she's been up to. You can hear how school's going, her holiday plans plus all about Genie and her crazy nans. ✤ There's a weekly round-up on hot topics in the news brought to you by Sniff, the friendly ITN newshound. ✤ Dot's cyberspace adventures are updated three times a week. ✤ Dot has plenty of help and advice for her dinosaur dad, so if you aren't up on all the internet terms you'll find these pages useful. (Of course, it's great for adults, too!) ✤ Thanks to Mister Mouse, Dot visits some really famous people through their computers. Find out more about them on her site. ✤ Safety is always important to Dot, so she makes sure there's details on where to get help when you need it, and how to stay safe. ✤ You'll also find loads of games, homework help, competitions and giveaways.

www.missdorothy.com

Dot the Brownie

Being a friendly, fun and lively person, Dot is of course a Brownie. Every month she has a special column in *Brownie* magazine telling everything she's been up to at Brownies. There's also an exciting page on Dot's site with a link to The Guide Association website. Dot loves to hear all about your Brownie news, so you can e-mail her in complete safety at dot@missdorothy.com. She always replies.

MissDorothy.Com Foundation

Dot knows it is very important to help others around the world so she has her very own charity for children. At the moment she is trying to help her disabled friend, Bongani, in South Africa. Bongani, or Bongi for short, often takes part in Dot's adventures. Bongi will leave school when he's 14 because there is no room left in the building for older pupils. His special needs school was designed to hold 150 pupils but now there are 380 children. Dot is trying to raise money to build a new school.

No internet?

As well as reading about Dot as a Brownie, there's a great book called *Dot Com's First Adventure*. It is all about how Dot got caught up in the internet world. Find out how she feels being sucked into the screen, and how she gets away from the cyber rats waiting with their computer virus.

Dot's friends

If you visit her site, you'll soon see that Dot has lots of friends. Her pet dog, Wizard, travels with her on her internet adventures, along with Cursor the cat and Mister Mouse. Bongani and Genie are two of her best friends.

More info

As well as e-mailing Dot, or visiting her website, you can write to her by snail mail at:
MissDorothy.Com Fan Club
PO Box 5963
Coggeshall
Colchester
CO6 1WW

Learn more

During her travels Dot is always learning new things about the internet. She likes sharing what she's found out with other children and adults. She thinks it's important to let others know about children's issues and help charities.

71

Animal friends

Make your own collection of animal friends. Pick the ones you want to make, or create your own.

You need

glass ❖ mixing bowl ❖ spoon ❖ salt ❖ white flour ❖ water ❖ damp cloth ❖ baking tray ❖ paintbrush ❖ paints (powder paint is best) ❖ pva glue

1 Measure one glassful of salt and two glassfuls of flour into the bowl. Mix well.

2 Make a hole in the middle. Add a glass of water. Mix well to make a dough.

3 Sprinkle some flour on the work surface. Knead the dough gently. Add a little more water if it gets crumbly, or more flour if it's too wet.

4 Make your animals. Put them on a baking tray and cook in the oven at 110°C/gas mark ¹/₄–¹/₂ for 30 minutes. Then 125°C/gas mark ¹/₂ for an hour or until dried.

⚠ Get an adult to help you with the oven.

5 Let them cool. If any bits have dropped off, stick them on with glue. Now they are ready to paint.

Cat

1 Make a ball of dough about 6cm big. Make another half the size.

2 Stick the small ball to the top of the big one by dabbing water on the edges that will touch. Gently push them together and smooth the join.

3 Make two ears and stick them in place with water. Smooth the joins.

4 Make a long tail and stick it in place.

5 Cook it, then paint when it is cool. Don't forget to add the whiskers.

Illustrated by Nick Diggory

72

Frog

1 Make an oval shape, slightly wider at one end, about 8cm long.

2 Make another one about 3cm long. Stick them together using water. Smooth the join.

3 Shape the head and body with your fingers. Add two round eyes.

4 Cut four frog's feet from the dough. Stick them to the body.

5 Cook it, then paint when it is cool.

Take a look at page 44 for all the facts on frogs.

Pig

1 Make two balls, one about 7cm, the other about 3cm. Stick them together with water and smooth the join.

2 Make four small balls about 1cm for the feet. Stick them in place.

3 Make two small ears and a tiny spiral tail. Stick them on. Carefully smooth the join using your little finger.

4 Cook it, then paint when it is cool.

Snail

1 Make a long sausage. Curl it into a spiral.

2 Make another sausage for the body. Flatten it slightly towards one end.

3 Stick the spiral on the flat area and smooth the join. Bend the other end of the body to make the neck and head.

4 Cook it, then paint when it is cool.

Finishing touch

Mix some pva glue with a little water. When the paint has dried give each animal a thin coat to make it shiny.

Golden years

This year is the Golden Jubilee to celebrate
Queen Elizabeth II's 50 years as sovereign.
Have a go at these fun golden puzzles.

Same crown

Which of these two
crowns are the same?

Nuggets

How many gold
nuggets can you find?

Illustrated by Phil Dobson

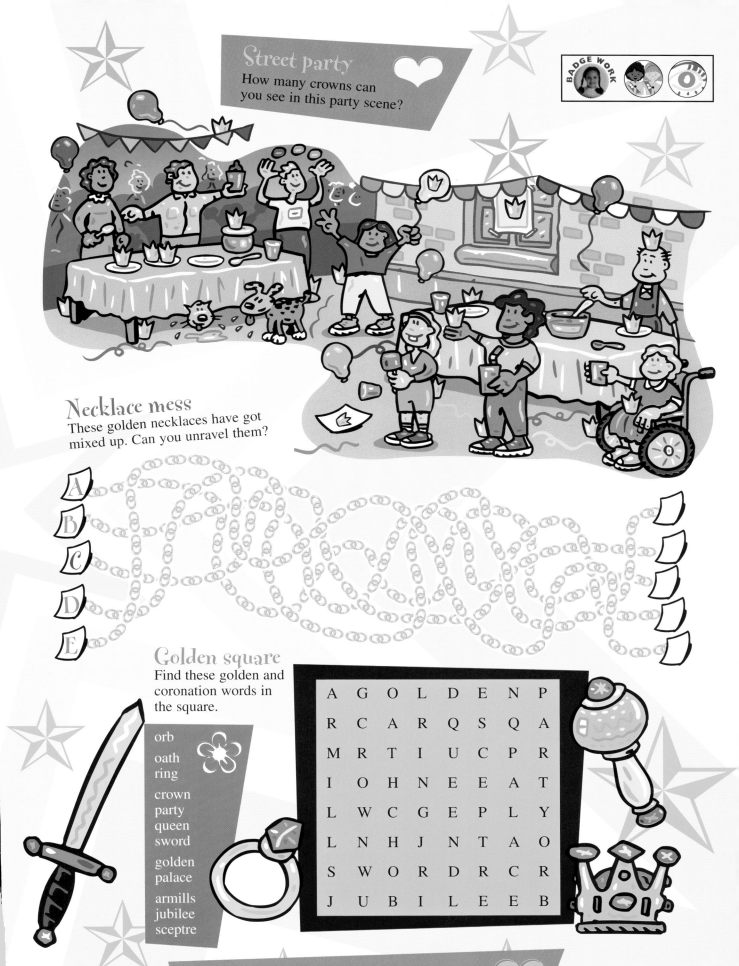

Street party

How many crowns can you see in this party scene?

Necklace mess

These golden necklaces have got mixed up. Can you unravel them?

A
B
C
D
E

Golden square

Find these golden and coronation words in the square.

orb
oath
ring

crown
party
queen
sword

golden
palace

armills
jubilee
sceptre

A	G	O	L	D	E	N	P
R	C	A	R	Q	S	Q	A
M	R	T	I	U	C	P	R
I	O	H	N	E	E	A	T
L	W	C	G	E	P	L	Y
L	N	H	J	N	T	A	O
S	W	O	R	D	R	C	R
J	U	B	I	L	E	E	B

Did you get a golden result? Take a look at page 76.

Answers

Starting maze
(inside front cover)

How well did you do at the puzzles in your **Brownie** Annual 2002?

Fever pitch
(page 16)

Spot the ball
There are 14 footballs in the park.

Find it out

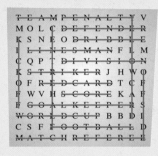

Odd ball

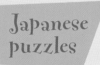

Get the goal

Get that word

Japanese puzzles
(page 32)

Same word

Noodled out
Clair has run out of noodle.

Pairs of sticks

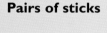

Karaoke night

Atomic Kitten	Point Break
Back Street Boys	Robbie Williams
Britney Spears	S Club 7
Craig David	Samantha Mumba
Daphne and Celeste	Spice Girls
Destiny's Child	Steps
Hear'say	Sugababes
	Westlife

Commonwealth capers
(page 42)

Make the gymnast
Piece B finishes the puzzle.

Longest jump

Cross country

Javelin spotting

Get into Guides
(page 58)

On the clothes
A and F are the same.

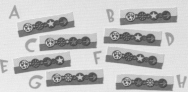

On the trail
There are other routes that work as well.

Muddled up
The Patrol names are:
Dolphin
Daffodil
Penguin
Thistle
Rose

Helping out
Zoe remembered to plug in her vacuum cleaner.

Zoe Fran
Anna Imogen Madison

Katie Jamilla

Holiday packing
Katie has a book, map and suncream. Jamilla has glasses, a magazine and travel guide.

Coded info
The Lion Patrol's messages are:
We're going camping next week.
Guides are great!
Let's have a party.
Last week's fashion show was excellent.

Pegged out
The Sphynx Patrol have lost 20 pegs.

Same crown

Nuggets
There are 15 nuggets.

Street party
There are 20 crowns.

Golden years
(page 74)

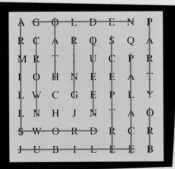

Golden square

Necklace mess

Join them up
shot putt
triple jump
track event
cross country
lawn bowls
table tennis
mountain biking
weight lifting

Hit the jack
Sam hit the jack.

Country search
Hidden in the word search is:
Commonwealth Games.

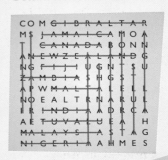

Illustrated by Phil Dobson, John Haslam and David Pattison